Foreword

Problems Galore is a blackline master with 50 pages of problem-solving activities for children from middle and upper primary. They will help children to organise their thoughts and working habits. The activities cover the important curriculum areas of:

- number;
- measurement; and
- space.

The activities can be done in any order and can be used in learning centres, as part of a whole-class activity, in small groups and for homework.

Many of the activities require few or no concrete materials apart from scissors or coloured pencils.

Contents

Square Number Puzzle	1	Noughts and Crosses	27
Paper Squares	2	Eight Circles	28
Addition Cross	3	Numbers and Squares	29
Squares and Squares	4	Lines and Crosses	30
Square Jigsaw	5	Five-by-Five Magic	31
Every Room	6	Cube Models	32
Houses and Paths	7	Joining Numbers	33
Tracing Squares	8	Adding in Squares	34
Dividing Shapes	9	Adding Primes	35
Amazing Addition	10	Consecutive Letters	36
Shape Puzzle	11	Patterns and Shapes	37
Five and Four Squares	12	Numbers and Paths	38
Seven and Five Squares	13	Paint Problem	39
Large Magic Squares	14	Cut and Make	40
Four Cubes	15	Paper Run	41
A Magic Hexagon	16	Going in Circles	42
What a Diamond!	17	Number Placement	43
Number Paths	18	Major Magic	44
Grid Colouring	19	Easy Addition	45
Consecutive Numbers	20	Adding Digits	46
Nine Squares	21	Triangle Addition	47
Time Addition	22	Make a Square	48
Octagon and Rectangle	23	Hexagon Magic	49
Squares and Paths	24	Minimum Colours	50
Dividing Shapes	25	Answers	51
Dividing Circles	26	Answers	52

Problems Galore

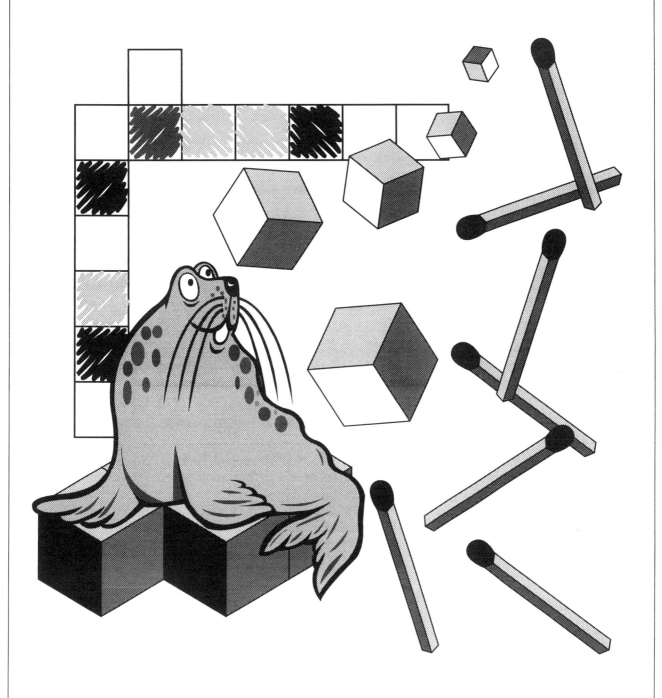

Prim-Ed Publishing

Write the digits 1 to 9 in the squares below. You may use each digit only once. All the equations going across and the equation going down must be correct.

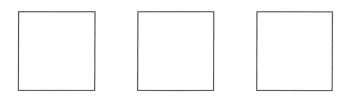

Can you rearrange the digits and equations to form another puzzle like the one above?

Paper Squares

A square which has been divided into sixteen smaller squares can be cut exactly in half in six different ways.

Two of the ways have been done for you below. Can you divide the four squares below into halves to show the other four methods?

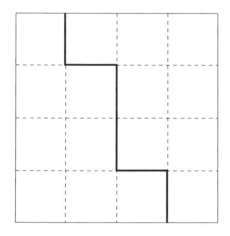

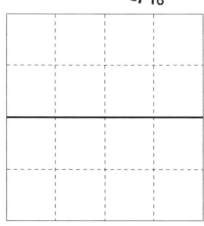

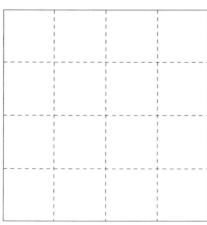

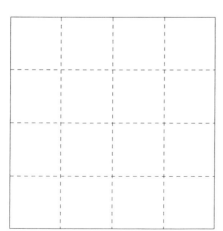

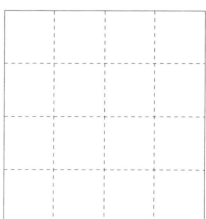

Addition Cross

Arrange the numbers 2 to 10 in the cross below so that the horizontal and vertical totals are equal to 32.

Using the same numbers as above with the crosses below, make one cross add up to 30 and the other to 28.

Squares and Squares

A square can easily be cut into four smaller squares.

It is a little more difficult to cut a square into six smaller squares.

Can you cut the squares below into seven and then eight smaller squares?

Square Jigsaw

Cut out the shapes below.
Put them together to make a square.

Every Room

Below is a plan of a house that has nine rooms. Can you walk through each of the nine rooms by crossing every wall just once?

| | 3 | 2 |

5

4

1

6

7

8

9

Houses and Paths

Below is a map of five houses joined by nine paths. Start at the first house and try to walk to all the other houses using each path only once. Can you do this?

You must remember to use all the paths, but only once.

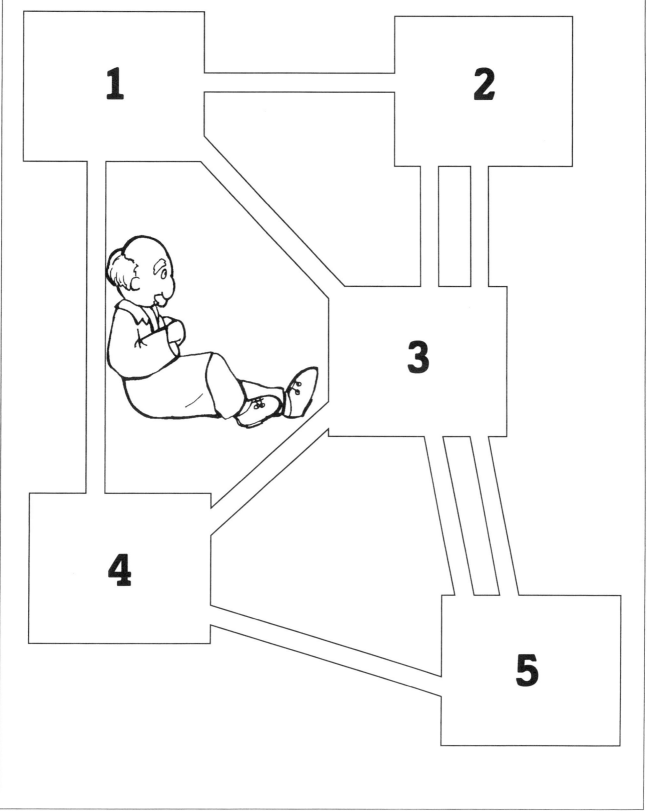

Tracing Squares

Trace over the diagram below, starting from the dot, without lifting your pencil from the paper and without tracing over the same line twice

Dividing Shapes

Divide the shape below into two, three and four identical pieces.

Two identical pieces

Three identical pieces

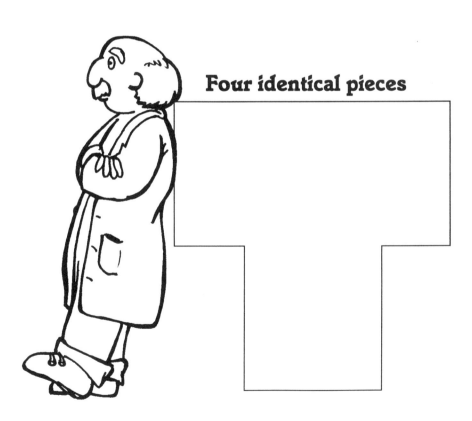

Four identical pieces

Amazing Addition

Using coloured pencils, try to find ways into the centre of the maze that add up to:

         16;
         25; and
         31.

What other totals can you come up with?

_____ _____ _____

_____ _____ _____

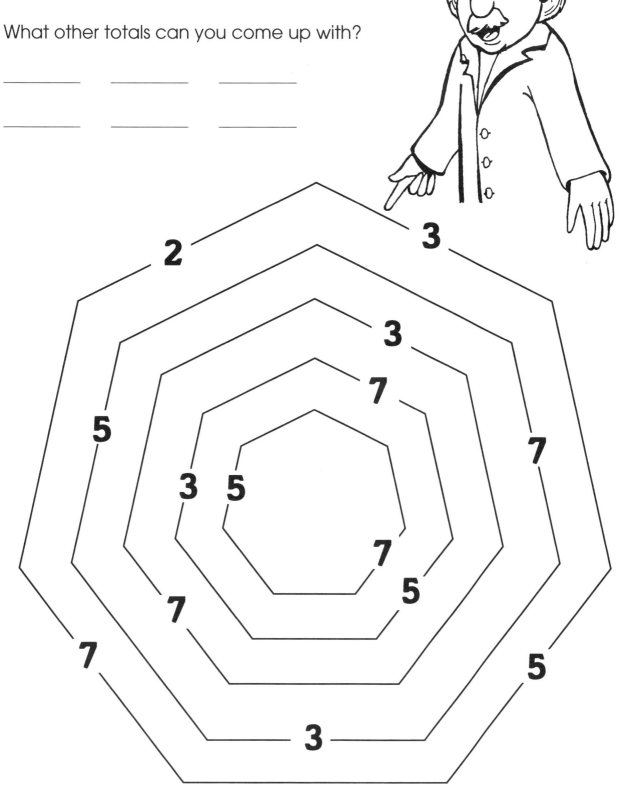

Shape Puzzle

Cut out the shapes below.
Rearrange them to make:

a square; and
a triangle.

Five and Four Squares

Make five squares using matches as shown below.
Move only two matches to reduce the number of squares from five to four.
Matches cannot overlap or be removed.

Seven and Five Squares

Make seven squares using matches as shown below.
Move only three matches to reduce the number of squares from seven to five.
Matches cannot overlap or be removed.

Large Magic Squares

Put the numbers 2, 3, 5, 8, 9, 12, 14 and 15 into the empty squares so that all the rows, columns and large diagonals add up to 34.

	11	6	
4			13
	7	10	
16			1

Put the numbers 2, 5, 7, 8, 11, 12, 14 and 17 into the empty squares so that all the rows, columns and large diagonals add up to 38.

10			9
	15	4	
6			13
	3	16	

Put the numbers 9, 12, 18, 27, 30, 39, 45 and 48 into the empty squares so that all the rows, columns and large diagonals add up to 114.

	36	21	
15			42
	24	33	
51			6

Four Cubes

Eight completely different objects can be made using four cubes. Each cube must be joined to another cube along at least one face. Turning, flipping or sliding a model does not make a new model. The four objects below are, in fact, only one answer.

Draw all eight answers in the boxes below.

A Magic Hexagon

Place the numbers 14 to 26 into the hexagon so that all the lines leading into the centre add up to 60.

What a Diamond!

Place eight of the numbers from 1 to 9 into the small diamonds below so that if you add the numbers:

- around the big diamond;
- around the small diamond;
- along the straight line across the diamonds; and
- along the straight line down the diamond;

your total will be 20 each time. (You may only use a number once.)

Number Paths

Join the numbers horizontally or vertically so that you make a continuous path connecting twelve numbers that add up to 174.

Make up your own paths and share them with other people.

16	**12**	**17**	**11**	**15**
13	**18**	**10**	**14**	**12**
17	**11**	**18**	**11**	**16**
10	**17**	**12**	**16**	**10**
16	**12**	**15**	**13**	**17**

Grid Colouring

Colour twelve of the squares in the grid below so that:

- there are no more than two per column;
- there are no more than two per row; and
- there are no more than two per diagonal.

Consecutive Numbers

Place the numbers 11 to 18 into the circles below so that no two consecutive numbers are in circles joined by a line.

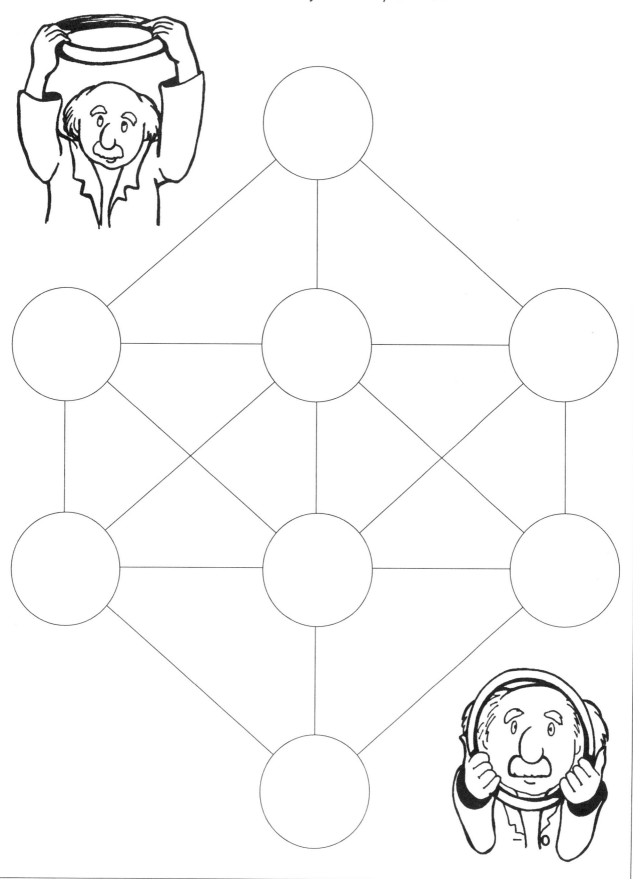

Nine Squares

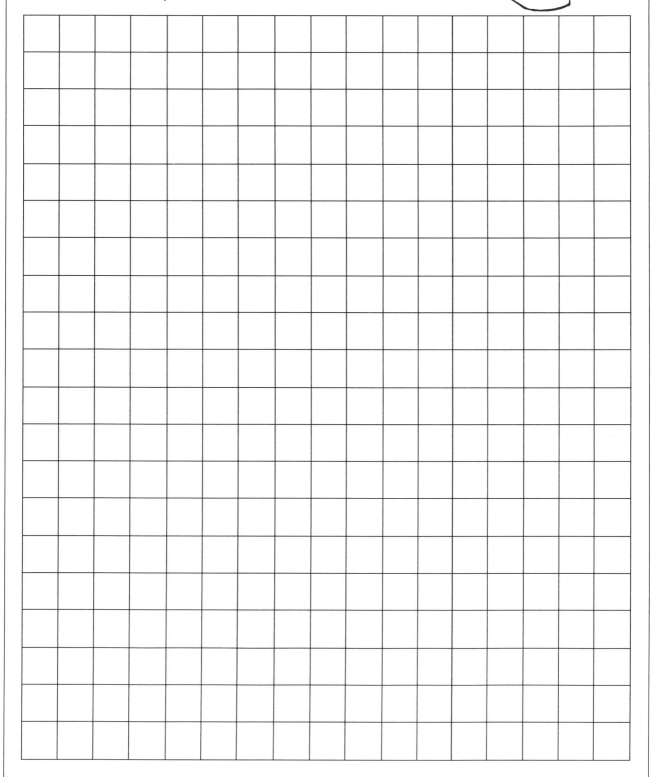

In the grid below, draw five shapes each with an area of nine squares. The shapes must have the following perimeters:

- Shape 1   Perimeter = 12;
- Shape 2   Perimeter = 14;
- Shape 3   Perimeter = 16;
- Shape 4   Perimeter = 18; and
- Shape 5   Perimeter = 20.

Time Addition

Use one straight line to divide the clock face below into two regions so that the sum of the numbers in each region is the same.

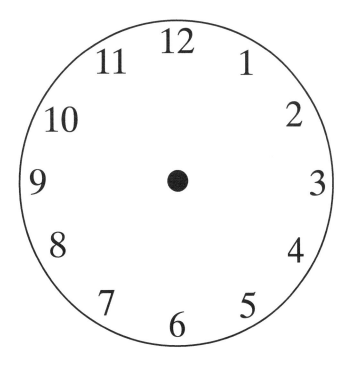

Use two straight lines to divide the clock face below into three regions so that the sum of the numbers in each region is the same.

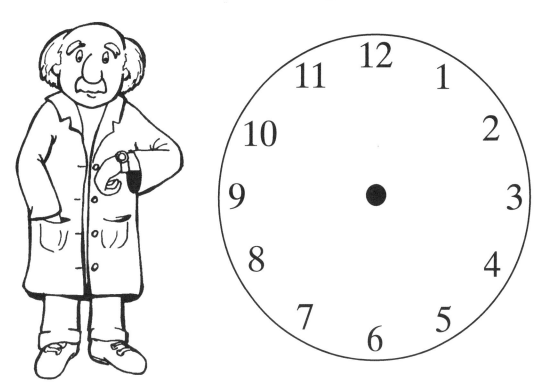

Octagon and Rectangle

Cut out the shapes below and rearrange them to make a rectangle and an octagon.

Squares and Paths

Join the squares to their corresponding squares with lines.

However, no lines may cross over another and you may not go outside the large square.

A B C D

D

A

C

B

Dividing Shapes

Divide the shape below into four.
Each quarter should be the same
size and shape.

Divide the shape below into four. Each quarter should be the same
size and shape.

Dividing Circles

Split the circle into two regions so that the sum of the numbers in each region is the same.

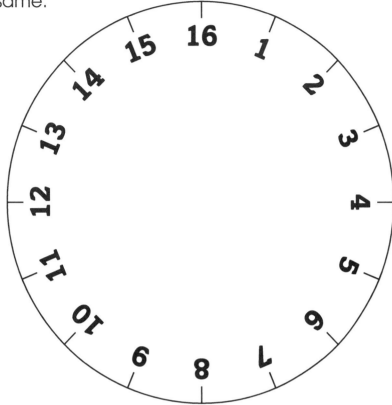

Split the circle into four regions so that the sum of the numbers in each region is the same.

Noughts and Crosses

Place ten noughts and six crosses on the grid below so that the rows and columns that are eight squares long each have two noughts and one cross in them.

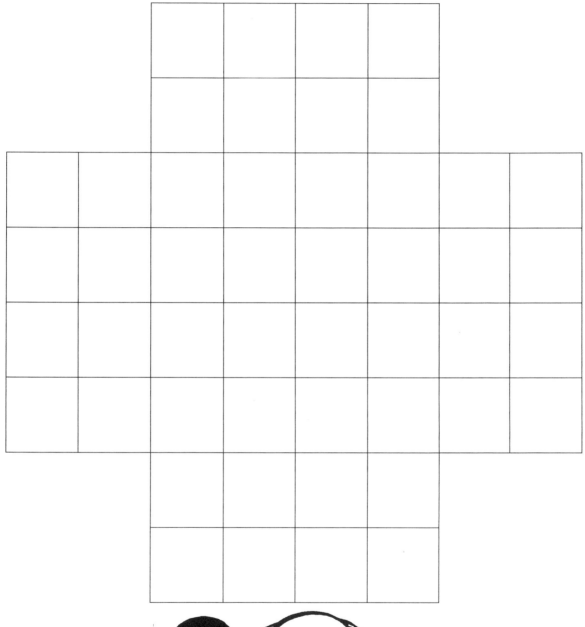

Eight Circles

Draw eight circles on the grid below so that:
- • every circle is in a different square;
- • there are no circles on the large diagonals of the grid; and
- • there is only one circle in a row and column.

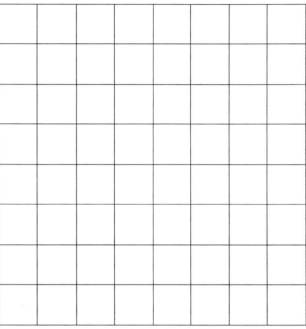

Draw eight circles on the grid below so that:
- • every circle is in a different square;
- • there are no circles on the large diagonals of the grid;
- • no circle shares any diagonal; and
- • there is only one circle in a row and column.

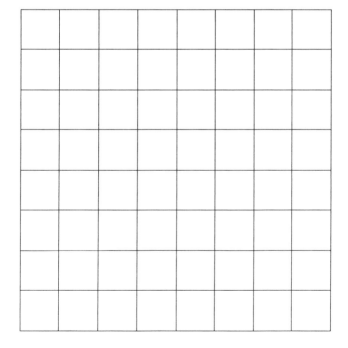

Numbers and Squares

Place the numbers 1, 2, 3, 4 and 5 into the grid so that each number appears in all rows, columns and large diagonals. You will need to use each number five times.

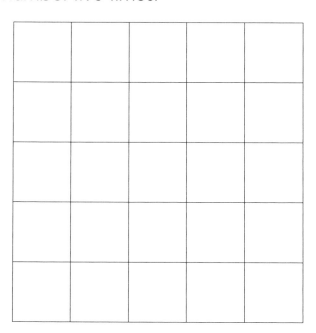

Place the numbers 1, 2, 3, 4, 5, 6 and 7 into the grid so that each number appears in all rows, columns and large diagonals. You will need to use each number seven times.

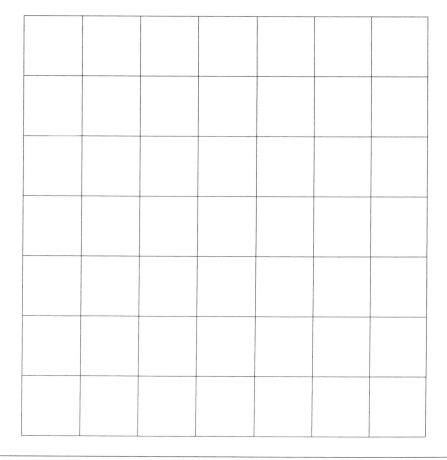

Lines and Crosses

Place nine crosses on the grid so that you can draw eight straight lines that each join three crosses.

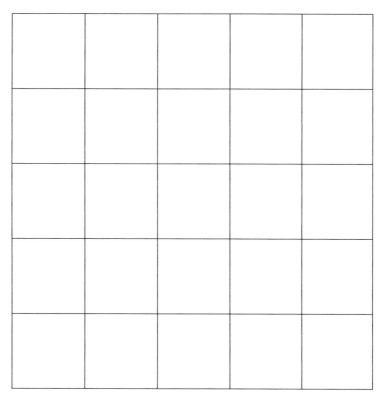

Rearrange the nine crosses on the grid so that you can draw nine straight lines that each join three crosses.

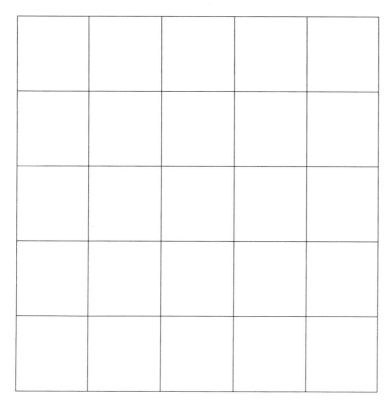

Five-by-Five Magic

Complete the magic square by placing the remainder of the numbers from 1 to 25 in the squares so that each column, row and large diagonal adds up to 65.

	24		8	15
	5			
		13		22
10	12	19		
		25	2	9

Complete the magic square by placing the remainder of the numbers from 13 to 37 in the squares so that each column, row and large diagonal adds up to 125.

29	36		20	
			26	
16		25		
		31	33	15
23	30	37		

Cube Models

How many cubes did it take to make the models below?

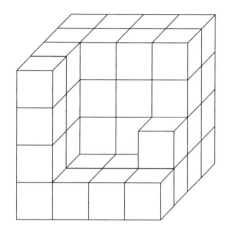

Model 1 took _____ cubes

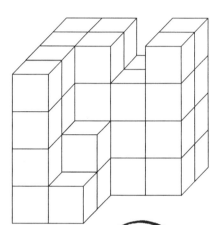

Model 2 took _____ cubes

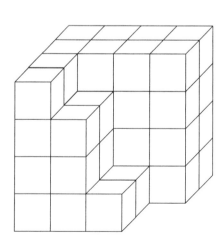

Model 3 took _____ cubes

Model 4 took _____ cubes

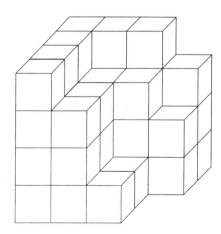

Joining Numbers

Join the number 1 to 1, 2 to 2, 3 to 3 and so on with straight lines along the grid. You must join all the numbers to their matching number but none of the paths may cross over.

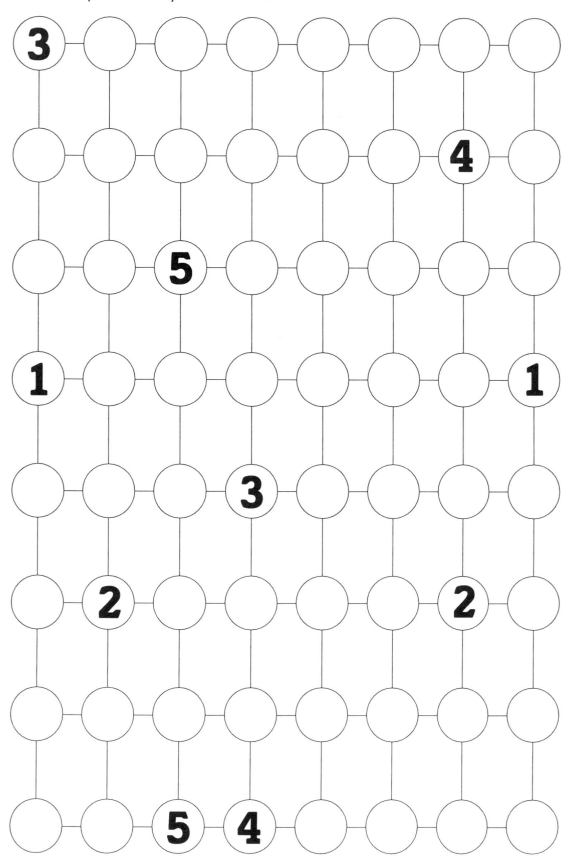

Adding in Squares

The four numbers in the grid have been added horizontally, vertically and diagonally. The answer to each addition sum has been written outside the grid.

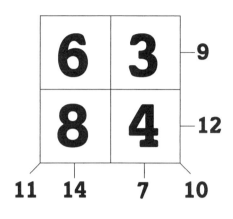

The same has been done for the grids below. Can you work out the numbers that need to be placed inside the grids?

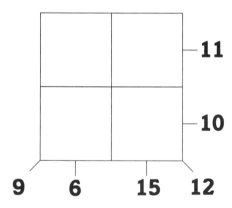

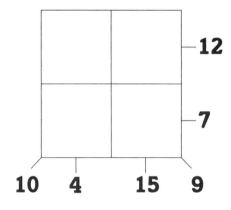

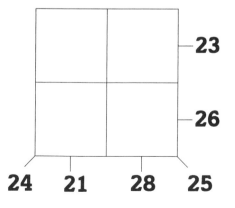

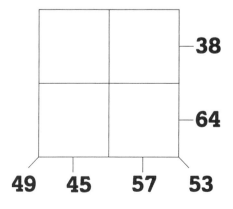

Adding Primes

Place all the prime numbers between 4 and 25 into the diagram below once, so that each of the columns and diagonals adds up to the same prime number.

What is the prime number? _____

Consecutive Letters

Place the letters A, B, C, D and E into the squares so that no two connected squares contain consecutive letters. For example, A cannot be next to B.

Try to find four different solutions.

Patterns and Shapes

Cut out the nine shapes below and rearrange them in the grid so that:
- no row or column has more than one similar shape; and
- no row or column has more than one type of shading.

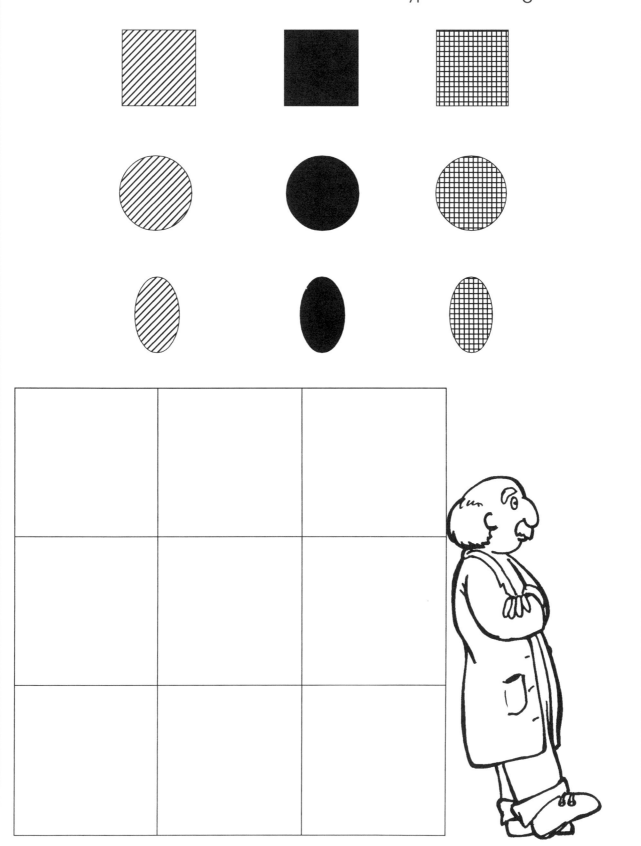

Numbers and Paths

Join the number 1 to 2 with a line.
Then do the same for 3 and 4, 5 and 6 and 7 and 8.

None of the lines may cross over each other.

1

4

2

5

3

7

6

8

Paint Problem

All the regions in the diagram below have an area of 8 cm², apart from the larger region at the bottom which has an area of 16 cm².

Your paints have only enough to paint the following areas:
- 16 cm² of blue;
- 24 cm² of yellow;
- 16 cm² of red; and
- 16 cm² of green.

Paint the diagram so that no two touching areas are the same colour. Two diagrams are provided as you will probably need them!

Cut and Make

Cut out the shapes below and rearrange them to make:

- a rectangle;
- a square;
- a triangle; and
- a parallelogram.

Paper Run

The map below is not to scale. It represents a newspaper factory, marked by the * and seven shops that sell newspapers, marked by the letters A to F. Work out the shortest route that could be taken to deliver newspapers to all the shops by starting and finishing at the factory.

How many kilometres is this route? _____

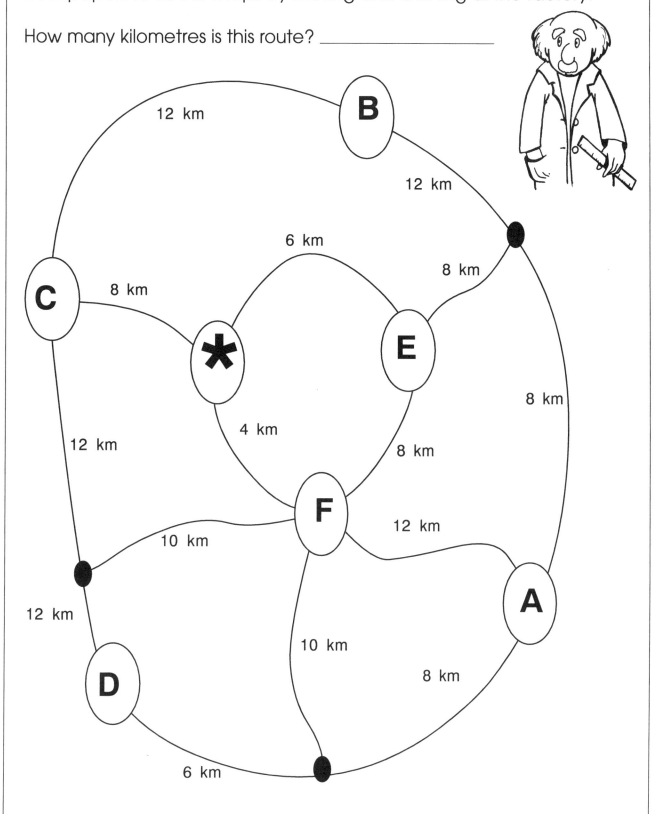

Going in Circles

Place the numbers 1 to 19 into the circles so that any three numbers joined by a line add up to the same number.

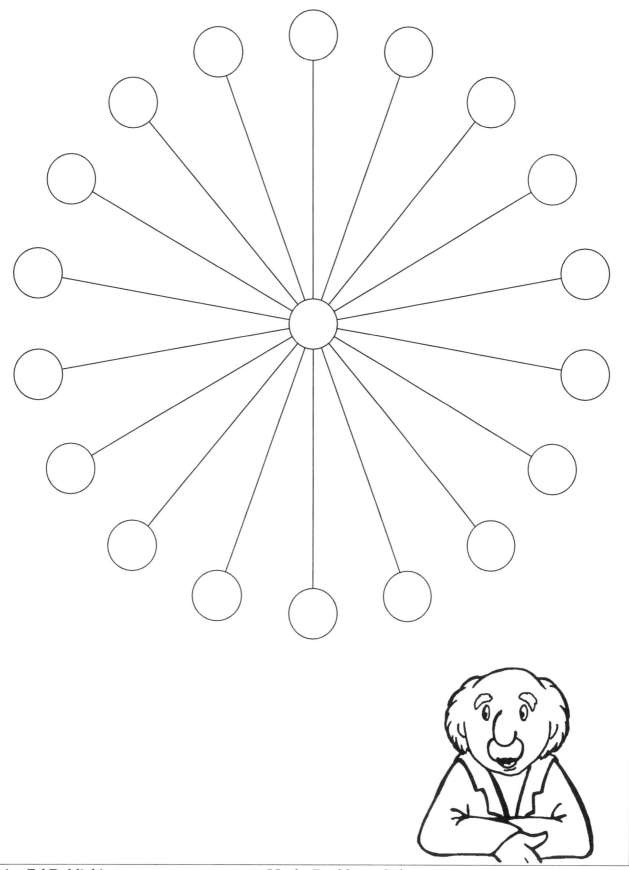

Place the numbers 11 to 19 in the grid below. Use each number only once. You must also use the following rules:

- row A has all even numbers;
- row B has all odd numbers;
- 12 and 16 are in the same column;
- 16 is not in the same row as 14; and
- 11 and 19 are in the same row.

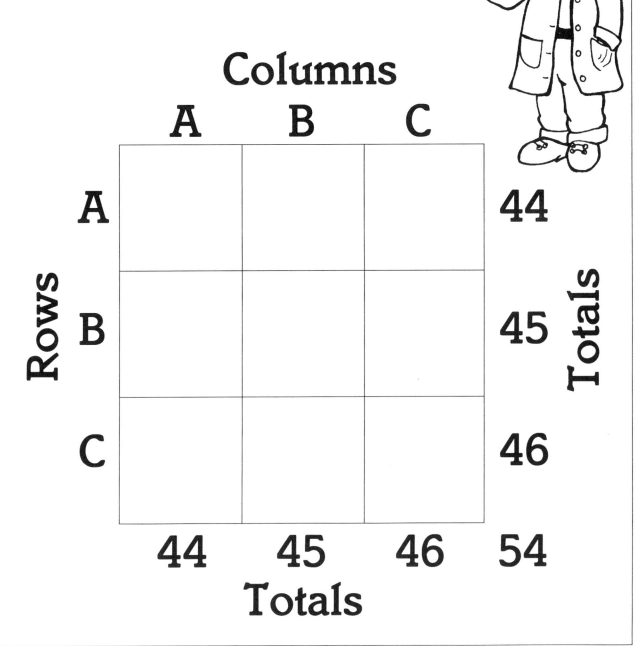

Columns

	A	B	C	Totals
A				44
B				45
C				46
Totals	44	45	46	54

Rows

Major Magic

Put the four squares together to make a 6 x 6 large magic square. Remember a magic square is one where the totals of each column, row and large diagonal add up to the same total or magic number. You may need to try many combinations.

What is the magic number? _____

49	8	21
2	41	30
45	12	17

43	14	15
6	37	34
47	10	19

1	42	29
48	9	20
5	38	33

7	36	35
44	13	16
3	40	31

Easy Addition

In the grid below, the numbers go from 2 to 144 in multiples of 2.

How many numbers appear on the grid? _____

What is the sum of all the numbers? _____

Hint: There is an easy way of doing this.

2	4	6	8	10	12	14	16
18	20	22	24	26	28	30	32
34	36	38	40	42	44	46	48
50	52	54	56	58	60	62	64
66	68	70	72	74	76	78	80
82	84	86	88	90	92	94	96
98	100	102	104	106	108	110	112
114	116	118	120	122	124	126	128
130	132	134	136	138	140	142	144

Adding Digits

Arrange the digits 1 to 9 into the squares to form a correct addition problem.

One answer is provided. Can you make up another four?

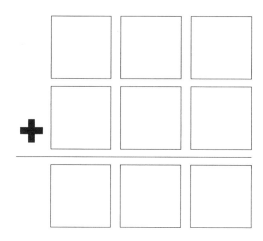

Triangle Addition

Place the numbers 5, 10, 15, 20, 25, 30, 35, 40, 45, 50, 55 and 60 into the circles to make each line in the two triangles add up to 130.

Make a Square

Cut out the shapes below and put them together to make one large square.

Hexagon Magic

Place the numbers 1 to 19 into the hexagons so that each of the 15 rows adds up to 38.

Minimum Colours

What is the minimum number of colours required to colour each of the diagrams below, so that no two touching areas have the same colour?

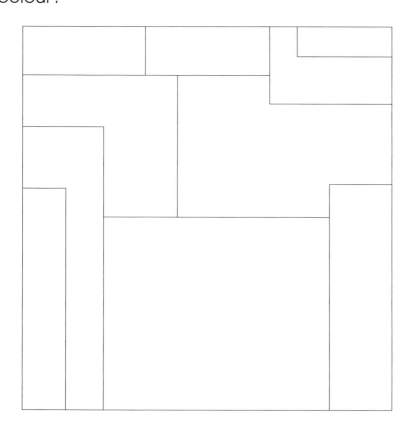

Page 1

Page 2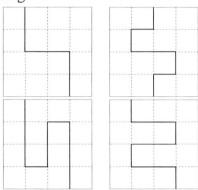

Page 3

Page 4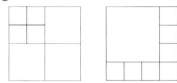

Page 5

Page 6

Page 7   No, it cannot be done.

Page 8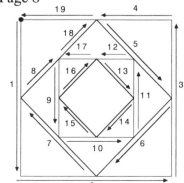

Page 9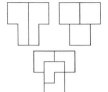

Page 10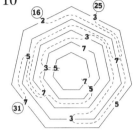

Page 11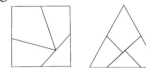

Page 12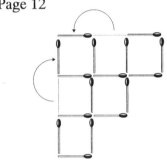

Page 13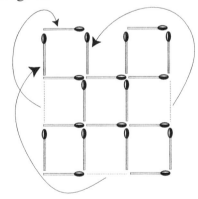

Page 14

34			
9	11	6	8
4	14	3	13
5	7	10	12
16	2	15	1

38			
10	12	7	9
5	15	4	14
6	8	11	13
17	3	15	2

114			
30	36	21	27
15	45	12	42
18	24	33	39
51	9	48	6

Page 15

Page 16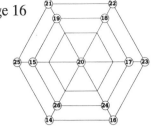

Page 17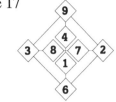

Page 18

Page 19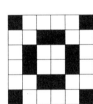

Page 20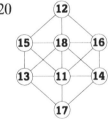

Page 21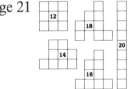

Page 22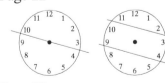

Page 23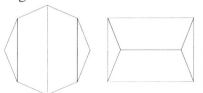

Page 24
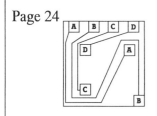

Page 25

Page 26

Page 27
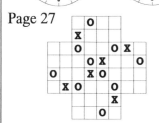

Page 28 -   There are other
answers
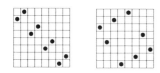

Page 29
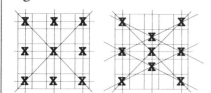

Page 30

Page 31

17	24	1	8	15
23	5	7	14	16
4	6	13	20	22
10	12	19	21	3
11	18	25	2	9

29	36	13	20	27
35	17	19	26	28
16	18	25	32	34
22	24	31	33	15
23	30	37	14	21

Page 32
Model 1 = 47; Model 2 = 41;
Model 3 = 48; Model 4 = 43;

Page 33
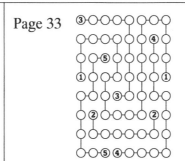

Page 34
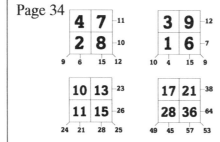

Page 35
The prime
number is 41.
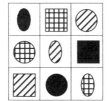

Page 36
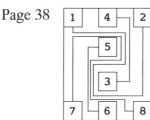

Page 37
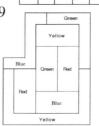

Page 38

Page 39

Page 40

Page 41

84 km
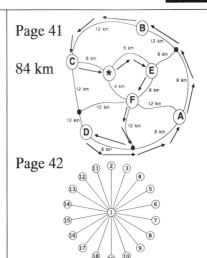

Page 42

Page 43   Page 44

Page 45
72 numbers appear on the grid.
36 number pairs, 2 + 144 = 146,
4 + 142 = 146 etc.
Total is 146 x 36 = 5 256.

Page 46 - Answers will vary.

Page 47
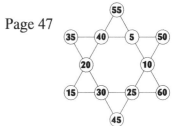

Page 48
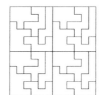

Page 49

Page 50
For the square you need three
colours.
For the circle you need five
colours.